DORA the EXPLORER®

Dora's Mystery of the Missing Shoes

by Christine Ricci
illustrated by Steve Savitsky

Ready-to-Read

SCHOLASTIC INC.

New York   Toronto   London   Auckland   Sydney
Mexico City   New Delhi   Hong Kong   Buenos Aires

Hi! I am .
DORA

I love playing in the ⬛.
SANDBOX

at 🎠.
PLAY PARK

The ☁ tickles my 👣!
SAND   TOES

likes 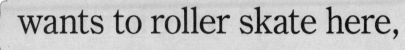 too!

SWIPER

PLAY PARK

 wants to roller skate here,

SWIPER

but something is missing.

What is missing?

SWIPER is missing a **SKATE**!

Look! My  is gone!

SNEAKER

We have to find the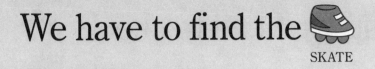
SKATE

and  .
SNEAKER

We will be detectives

and solve this mystery!

First, we need to check 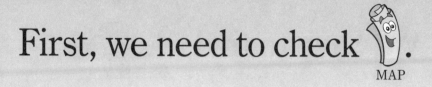. MAP

 says that the  and

MAP   SKATE   SNEAKER

are in the .

FIELD

We need to go through the

 and across the 🏵️.

CAVE   POND

BACKPACK has everything we need to be detectives.

Will you find a **MAGNIFYING GLASS**?

We need the
MAGNIFYING GLASS

to find the tiny
ROCKS

that lead to the .
CAVE

The  is dark.
CAVE

I see a shadow!

What could it be?

It is .
BOOTS

What is 🐵 missing?
BOOTS

🐵 is missing his 👢 !
BOOTS   BOOT

We made it to the .

POND

Look at the !

WAVES

Who is making the ?

WAVES

is making the ⁀ .

BENNY   WAVES

 is swimming.

BENNY

But what is missing?

BENNY

BENNY is missing his **FLIPPER**!

BOOTS is missing his **BOOT**.

SWIPER is missing his **SKATE**.

I am missing my **SNEAKER**.

We have to get to the  FIELD

to solve this mystery.

Do you see the FIELD?

Here at the  I see

FIELD

HAY , COWS , and WAGONS .

Look closely!

Do you see a ,
SKATE

a
BOOT

, and a
FLIPPER

?

Who is wearing

the  ,   ,   , and   ?
SKATE   SNEAKER   BOOT   FLIPPER

It is a little   !
HORSE

The , and got stuck on the 's feet.

SKATE   SNEAKER   BOOT   FLIPPER

HORSE

It was a mistake!

We solved the mystery!

This  needs
HORSE

her own shoes.

Do you see 4 🧲🧲?

FOUR HORSESHOES

The  is happy

HORSE

to have her own  !

HORSESHOES

We are glad to have

our things back!

Thanks for helping!